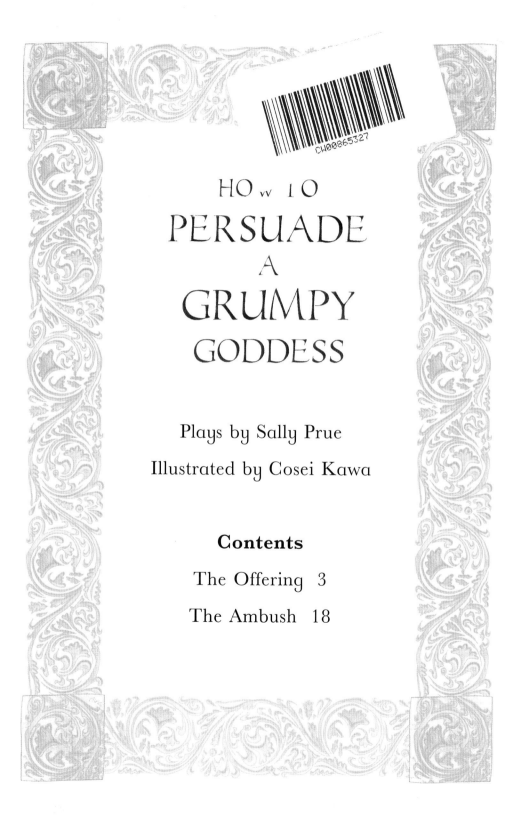

# HOw 1O PERSUADE A GRUMPY GODDESS

Plays by Sally Prue

Illustrated by Cosei Kawa

## Contents

Published by Pearson Education Limited, Edinburgh Gate, Harlow, Essex, CM20 2JE.

www.pearsonschools.co.uk

Text © Sally Prue 2013
Designed by Sara Rafferty
Original illustrations © Pearson Education Limited 2013
Illustrated by Cosei Kawa

The right of Sally Prue to be identified as author of this work has been asserted by her in accordance with the Copyright, Designs and Patents Act 1988.

First published 2013

17 16 15 14 13
10 9 8 7 6 5 4 3 2 1

British Library Cataloguing in Publication Data
A catalogue record for this book is available from the British Library

ISBN 978 0 435 14421 0

Printed and bound in Dubai by Oriental Press

**Acknowledgements**
We would like to thank Bangor Central Integrated Primary School, Northern Ireland; Bishop Henderson Church of England Primary School, Somerset; Bletchingdon Parochial Church of England Primary School, Oxfordshire; Brookside Community Primary School, Somerset; Bude Park Primary School, Hull; Carisbrooke Church of England Primary School, Isle of Wight; Cheddington Combined School, Buckinghamshire; Dair House Independent School, Buckinghamshire; Deal Parochial School, Kent; Glebe Infant School, Goucestershire; Henley Green Primary School, Coventry; Lovelace Primary School, Surrey; Our Lady of Peace Junior School, Slough; Tackley Church of England Primary School, Oxfordshire; and Twyford Church of England School, Buckinghamshire for their invaluable help in the development and trialling of the Bug Club resources.

Every effort has been made to contact copyright holders of material reproduced in this book. Any omissions will be rectified in subsequent printings if notice is given to the publishers.

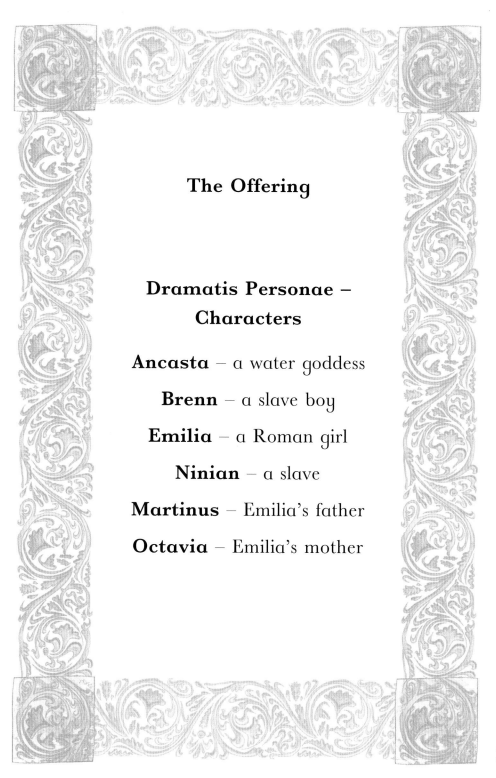

# The Offering

## Dramatis Personae – Characters

**Ancasta** – a water goddess

**Brenn** – a slave boy

**Emilia** – a Roman girl

**Ninian** – a slave

**Martinus** – Emilia's father

**Octavia** – Emilia's mother

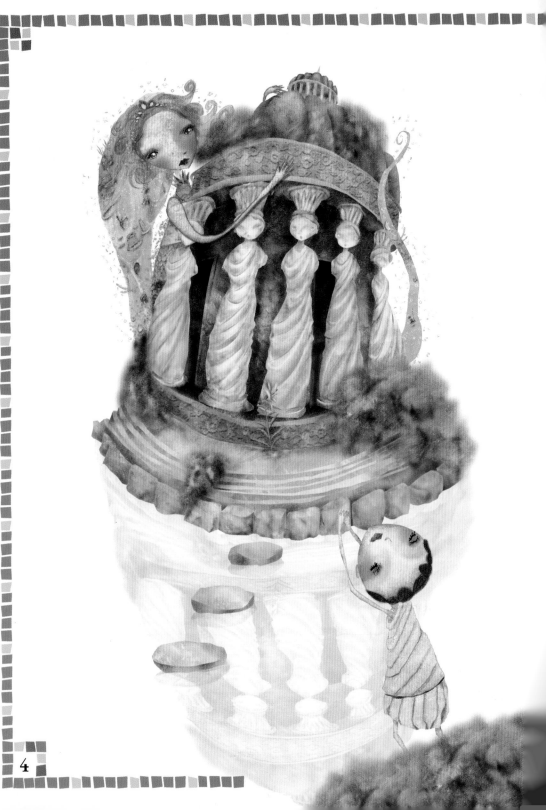

*Roman Britain. At the shrine of the water goddess, Ancasta, in the grounds of a large Roman villa.*

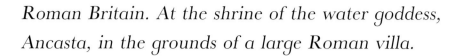 **Brenn:** Oh, great God of the shrine.

**Ancasta:** I'm not a god, I'm a **goddess**, silly boy!

**Brenn:** I'm only a slave, oh God, but please help me.

**Ancasta:** I'm a **goddess**!

**Brenn:** Please, oh God, make Martinus set me free.

**Ancasta:** I'm a ... Oh, what's the **point**? These stupid humans can never hear a word I say.

**Brenn:** I haven't any gold to offer you.

**Ancasta:** That doesn't bother me. Gold tastes disgusting.

**Brenn:** But I could find you some nice ... pebbles. Oh bother. I'm never going to be set free at this rate, am I?

*Emilia enters.*

**Emilia:** Moaning **again**, Brenn!

**Ancasta:** He's always moaning.

**Emilia:** Honestly, Brenn, I don't know why you keep complaining. It's lovely living here.

**Brenn:** Not if you're a slave.

**Emilia:** You wouldn't have under-floor heating if you were still living in a Celtic hut, you know. Or cake.

**Ancasta:** Cake! He gets cake! And all they give me is stupid gold.

**Emilia:** And you wouldn't have the animal shows either.

**Brenn:** Huh! The only way **I'll** get to go to an animal show is if they feed me to the lions!

*Martinus approaches.*

**Martinus:** Ninian! Drat, where is that thieving slave?

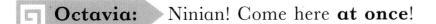

**Octavia:** Ninian! Come here **at once**!

**Emilia:** Mother and Father sound annoyed.
I wonder what Ninian has done now?

*Martinus and Octavia approach.*

**Martinus:** Have you seen Ninian, slave boy?

**Brenn:** No, Master.

**Ancasta:** I can't think why you want Ninian.
He's really smelly. And he's a thief.

7

**Octavia:** My gold comb has gone missing. You haven't borrowed it, have you, Emilia?

**Emilia:** No, Mother.

**Martinus:** Never mind your comb; there's a purse of gold coins missing, too.
Ninian! NINIAN!

**Ninian:** Master?

**Octavia:** At last. Where's my comb?

**Ninian:** Your comb?

**Emilia:** It's a thing to prevent people's hair looking like yours does, Ninian.

**Martinus:** And where's my purse? Speak up, you miserable slave!

**Ninian:** I haven't seen a comb or a purse anywhere, Master. Not all the time I've been working.

**Ancasta:** No? That's because you stole them when you were slacking, isn't it?

**Octavia:** What's that in your hand?

**Ninian:** Only a cloth, Mistress. I've been polishing the floors all morning.

**Emilia:** No you haven't. I saw you hanging about down by the hedge.

**Ninian:** Ah. Yes. Well. I was helping the laundry slaves hang the washing on the hedge, young Mistress.

**Martinus:** That's the most unlikely thing I've ever heard in my life. You slaves are all lazy. **And** you're always eating.

**Ancasta:** None of them are as greedy as you, though, Martinus.

**Emilia:** Oh, Father! **Brenn** isn't lazy. He's always running about.

**Brenn:** Yes. Otherwise I get beaten.

**Octavia:** Well, the only time Ninian ever runs anywhere is if he sees something to eat.

**Martinus:** You're right, Octavia. He's completely useless. I think I'll banish him to the mines.

**Ninian:** No! Not the mines, Master! Please! Not honest Ninian!

**Ancasta:** Honest? You're the most weaselly slave in the district.

**Ninian:** You don't even know that I was the one who stole your things!

**Octavia:** That's true, Martinus. It could have been any of the slaves.

**Martinus:** Very well. Then I'll send **all** the slaves to the mines!

**Brenn:** **All** of us? But Master …

**Emilia:** Oh Father, not Brenn. Not the mines. Who will wash my clothes?

**Ancasta:** And clean my shrine?

**Ninian:** Master! I've just realised who the thief must be! There was … er … a man. This morning. Lurking by the gate.

**Octavia:** He's lying, Martinus.

**Ninian:** No, I'm not. He was really dodgy. He had a big beard!

**Emilia:** And an enormous bag with SWAG written on it, didn't he, Ninian?

**Ninian:** Yes, an enormous bag with … er …

**Brenn:** What are you talking about, Ninian?

**Octavia:** As if anyone would believe that.

**Martinus:** I'll soon get a confession out of him.

**Octavia:** No, Martinus, you'll tire yourself. We'll go and call the guards. They'll soon make Ninian talk. Come along!

*Octavia and Martinus exit.*

**Emilia:** Oh, Brenn. What do we do now?

**Brenn:** I'll be dead in a month if I'm sent down a mine!

**Ninian:** And so will I!

**Ancasta:** Yes, but no one cares about you.

**Emilia:** Look, Ninian, give the stuff back. Perhaps then …

**Ninian:** But I can't!

**Brenn:** Why not? You've hidden it in the hedge, haven't you?

**Ninian:** Yes. But I threw some of the gold in the pond, to the god of the shrine so he'd help me escape.

**Ancasta:** "**She'd** help me escape." I'm a **goddess**!

*Martinus, Octavia and the guards approach.*

**Martinus:** Come along, you men! This way!

**Octavia:** He's at the shrine!

**Emilia:** Oh no! Here are Mother and Father coming back.

**Brenn:** Look, I'll go and fetch the stuff from the hedge. You two keep them talking – and pray like mad!

13

**Ninian:** Oh please, please, please, great God, help me!

**Emilia:** She's a **goddess**!

**Ancasta:** At last! Thank you, Emilia.

**Ninian:** Really? Oh. Well, great Goddess, then. **Get me out of this**!

**Ancasta:** I don't see why I should. What have humans ever done for me? You lot live a life of luxury and I end up stuck in the bottom of a pool eating frogs and pond weed.

**Martinus:** Ninian!

**Octavia:** Don't let the guards make a mess at the shrine, dear.

| | |
|---|---|
| **Emilia:** | Father, wait just a minute. Ninian's saying his prayers. |
| **Martinus:** | I expect he is. |
| **Ninian:** | Please, Goddess. I'll give you anything. **Anything**! |
| **Ancasta:** | No you won't. You haven't got anything. You're just a lying weaselly slave. |
| **Brenn:** | Master! Master! Look! |
| **Martinus:** | Brenn! Your clothes are all torn. What have you been doing? |
| **Brenn:** | Fighting the man with the big beard, Master. And look! |
| **Octavia:** | My comb! And the purse! |
| **Ancasta:** | So that makes Brenn another lying weaselly human. |
| **Martinus:** | Hmm. Let's count the gold coins, shall we? Pass me the purse. |
| **Emilia:** | Let me count them, Father. |

*Brenn whispers.*

| | |
|---|---|
| **Brenn:** | Goddess! Help! |

15

**Ancasta:** No chance.

**Octavia:** **I'll** count them. One, two ...

**Brenn:** **Please, Goddess**. I'll bring you ... things.

**Ancasta:** Huh!

**Emilia:** Money.

**Ancasta:** Yawn.

**Ninian:** Er ... cake!

**Ancasta:** Cake? Oh. Well, in that case ...

**Brenn:** Look! The gold coins! They're floating up to the surface! Grab them Emilia!

**Emilia:** Father! Look, here are the rest of the gold coins! Brenn must have dropped them. You'll have to give him a reward now, won't you?

**Octavia:** I think we will.

**Martinus:** Oh ... Oh, all right. I'll grant you your freedom, Brenn.

**Brenn:** What? Really? But ... I won't have to leave the villa, will I?

**Martinus:** Not if you want to stay.

**Emilia:** But don't you **want** to leave, Brenn?

**Brenn:** What, and live somewhere without under-floor heating? You must be joking!

# FINIS

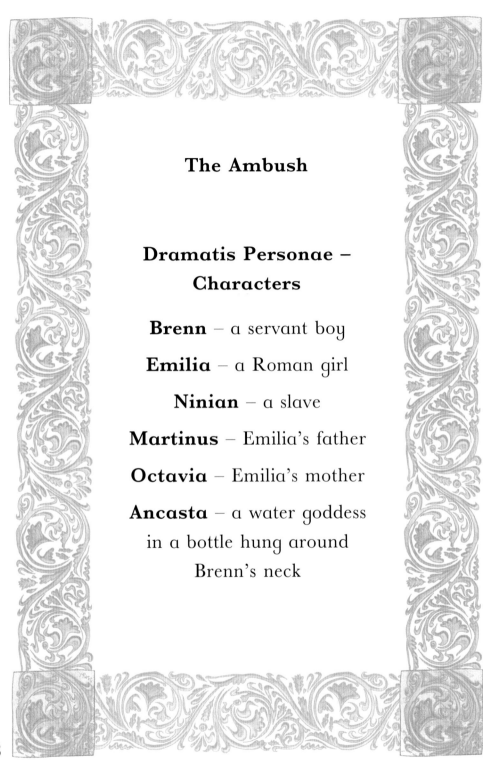

# The Ambush

## Dramatis Personae – Characters

**Brenn** – a servant boy

**Emilia** – a Roman girl

**Ninian** – a slave

**Martinus** – Emilia's father

**Octavia** – Emilia's mother

**Ancasta** – a water goddess
in a bottle hung around
Brenn's neck

*Roman Britain. Martinus, Octavia and Emilia are passengers in a reda (a horse-drawn carriage). Their servant Brenn and slave Ninian are travelling on foot beside the vehicle.*

**Martinus:** I don't know why I have to wear this ridiculous toga, anyway.

**Octavia:** You can't arrive at Livia's party looking like a servant, Martinus.

**Martinus:** I bet the servants are much more comfortable than I am. Togas, huh! They'll have men wearing bows round their throats next.

**Ancasta:** These humans! Moan, moan, moan! Here I am, stuck inside a bottle round Brenn's neck, and you don't catch **me** complaining!

**Emilia:** Never mind, Father. Think of the lovely food.

**Octavia:** Mm. Livia gave us dormice last time.

**Martinus:** Dormice? Nothing but bones.

**Emilia:** We've stopped. What's happened?

**Octavia:** I hope the horses are all right.
*(She shouts.)*
Slave! What's going on?

**Ninian:** Mistress! Help! Quick, let me into the reda!

**Octavia:** Open the door, Emilia.

**Ninian:** Quick! Hide me!

**Martinus:** Ow! Ow! Get out from under my seat, you wretch!

**Emilia:** What's the matter, Ninian?

**Ninian:** Celts, Mistress! Ten of them! On the hill!

*Brenn climbs into the reda.*

**Brenn:** Help, Master!

**Martinus:** Not you as well, Brenn. Get out of the reda, both of you. There's no room to breathe with all of us in it.

**Brenn:** But Master, there are Celts up on the hill!

**Octavia:** Well, I expect they're going to visit the market, Brenn.

**Ninian:** No, no, they're covered in woad!

**Emilia:** What's woad?

**Brenn:** War-paint.

**Emilia:** You mean they're planning to attack us?

**Martinus:** I knew it was madness, bringing the reda along a lonely road like this. And all for a bony dormouse!

**Ninian:** Oh save me, Master, save me! I'm too young to die!

**Martinus:** Get off me! Get off me!

**Octavia:** There are ten of them, you say? Well, we have twelve guards, so ...

**Brenn:** I'm afraid the others have all run away, Mistress. There are only two of us left.

**Martinus:** What? That means there's nothing to stop those brutes coming down here and slitting all our throats!

**Octavia:** Heaven save us!

**Emilia:** Oh Brenn! Can't you think of something?

**Brenn:** Er ... well, this little bottle here has some water from the goddess Ancasta's shrine in it. So I suppose we could try praying.

**Ancasta:** It's a bit squashed in here, but I enjoy the change of scene.

| | |
|---|---|
| **Emilia:** | Oh, great Goddess, please help us. |
| **Ninian:** | Please! **Please**! |
| **Ancasta:** | Don't look at me. I can't do anything. I'm a water goddess. I don't **do** battles. |

| | |
|---|---|
| **Octavia:** | Perhaps ... perhaps they're **nice** Celts, after all. I hear some Celts are quite civilised nowadays. |
| **Brenn:** | I think that lot are too hairy to be civilised, Mistress. |
| **Ancasta:** | Brenn's an idiot, but he's right this time. They look a nasty bunch. |

**Martinus:** I'm afraid the woad means they're probably Silures, Octavia.

**Octavia:** Silures? Oh, Martinus.

**Ancasta:** Silures? I used to know their god. Ocelus, they called him. A real scream, old Ocelus. The stories he told about the ways the Silures kill people! Enough to make a weasel laugh. I'd tell you all about it if you could only hear me.

**Emilia:** Oh, Brenn. What do we do now?

**Brenn:** Er ... well, how about if Ninian puts on your toga, Master, and then lets the Celts see him? Then they'll chase after Ninian and we can escape.

**Ninian:** What?

**Octavia:** That might just work, Martinus!

**Ninian:** Now, hang on ...

**Martinus:** Good idea, Brenn. I'll be plenty warm enough in my tunic.

**Ninian:** But ...

**Martinus:** Here's my toga, Ninian. Wrap yourself up.

**Ninian:** But ... why me?

**Emilia:** Because Brenn's too small.

**Ancasta:** And Martinus is too fat.

**Ninian:** Yes, but **I'm** too cowardly!

**Ancasta:** That's true.

**Octavia:** Oh dear! What can we do?

**Martinus:** Leave it to me, Octavia. Ninian, old friend. Now – you're a coward, we all know that, but you're greedy too, aren't you? If you do this little thing for us then you can have all this gold. And I'll grant you your freedom, too.

**Brenn:** Just think, Ninian, gold and freedom.

**Octavia:** We'll be so grateful, dear Ninian.

**Ninian:** Oh no! I don't do brave things. A coward I am, and a coward I'm staying.

**Emilia:** Then we will all die!

**Ancasta:** So what? It's what you humans do.

**Martinus:** Ninian, if you don't get out there this minute then when we get home I'll send you to the lions!

**Ninian:** What? Not the **lions**! Master, surely you wouldn't!

**Ancasta:** Ninian, fighting lions? He'd be rubbish. If he so much as smelled a lion, he'd drop dead from fright.

**Brenn:** Listen, Ninian, you don't have to be brave. You just have to crawl a long way away, let the Silures see you, and then run like crazy.

**Ninian:** I ... I've got no choice, have I?

**Martinus:** No.

**Brenn:** I'm sorry, Ninian.

**Ninian:** Well ... it's goodbye, then. Remember poor, devoted Ninian.

*Ninian exits.*

**Octavia:** Good heavens. He's actually gone.

**Emilia:** He's not nearly as weaselly as I thought.

**Ancasta:** Well, I'm amazed.

**Martinus:** A brave, devoted slave.

**Brenn:** I always said …

**Ninian:** Help! Help! Let me back in! Quick!

**Emilia:** Open the door!

**Brenn:** Ninian, what happened?

**Ninian:** I had to come back because ... ouch! Because of my bad leg.

**Octavia:** Nonsense, Ninian. You ran back here fast enough.

**Martinus:** Right. That does it, slave. It's the lions for you.

**Ninian:** **No! No! Not the lions!**

**Brenn:** Ninian. Calm down. Look ... we'll try again. And I'll come with you.

**Emilia:** Oh Brenn!

**Martinus:** Good idea.

**Octavia:** You'll not regret it, Brenn.

**Ancasta:** He will if the Silures get him.

**Brenn:** Well. So. Goodbye, everyone. Come **on**, Ninian.

**Octavia:** Brave, brave Brenn! Can you see them, Emilia?

**Emilia:** Yes. They're crawling up the hill.

**Brenn:** Come **on**, Ninian!

**Ninian:** I can't. My knees are knocking together too hard.

**Ancasta:** Those Silures will think they're being stalked by a woodpecker.

**Brenn:** Oh **Ninian**! Well, I suppose I'll have to go on alone, then.

**Emilia:** Brenn's going on alone!

**Octavia:** Such a wonderful boy.

**Brenn:** Yes, they're definitely Silures. Thank the goddess for that. Right, here goes, then. HEY! SILURES! THERE'S SOMETHING YOU NEED TO KNOW!

*A short time later.*

**Emilia:** They're back!

**Martinus:** What happened?

**Ancasta:** Brenn's cleverer than I thought.
And more cunning.

**Octavia:** Have the Celts gone?

**Brenn:** Yes, Mistress. We're safe!

**Ninian:** They've gone right away!

**Emilia:** Oh, Mother! Isn't Brenn wonderful?

**Octavia:** Yes, Emilia. Martinus, we must
adopt him.

**Martinus:** Adopt **Brenn**?

**Ninian:** You should have seen those Silures. There were
loads of them, all dark-haired and squat.

**Emilia:** Dark-haired and squat? Who does that
remind me of? Brenn!

**Brenn:** What?

**Octavia:** I'd like a son like Brenn, Martinus.

**Martinus:** Like **Brenn**?

*Emilia whispers to Brenn.*

**Emilia:** You're Silures yourself, aren't you?

**Brenn:** Shh!

**Emilia:** So how did you get rid of them?

**Ancasta:** He lied!

**Brenn:** I told them the reda was full of Roman soldiers.

**Ancasta:** And they believed him because he's Silures.

**Martinus:** I must admit that Brenn is a fine boy, Octavia.

**Octavia:** A fine **son**, Martinus.

**Emilia:** But ... Brenn ... why did you help us, and not your own people?

**Brenn:** The way things are going, Emilia, it looks as if you **are** my own people.

FINIS